Happy Together

a single father by choice
egg donation and surrogacy story

Written by Julie Marie

Illustrated by Ashley Lucas

This book is dedicated to MK and all that never was...

Happy Together

a single father by choice
egg donation and surrogacy story

Written by Julie Marie

Illustrated by Ashley Lucas

The sun was shining bright
And the sky was blue above,

Daddy had a happy life full of friends
And family with lots and lots of love.

Daddy went on many adventures
Laughing, smiling and having fun,

I had a great future ahead and wanted
To share it with a special little someone.

Deep within my heart
Daddy had a special wish
More than anything I wanted to have a baby
To love, hug and kiss!

For some parents
It's easy to have a baby
And for some parents
It's not.
For your Daddy
I knew my journey to have you
Would take a lot.

To make a baby
It takes a seed of a male
And an egg and tummy of a female.
Daddy had the seed
But I didn't have the egg
Or the special tummy.

Daddy went to a doctor
And asked for the help of two special ladies.

One special lady is called a donor
And she gave the egg.

The other special lady is called a surrogate
And the baby would grow in her tummy.

The doctor combined

Daddy's seed

With the donor's egg

Then he transferred it

Into the surrogate's tummy

And it turned out to be exactly what

I would need!

The sun was shining bright one day
The sky was blue above
That's when Daddy received the best news
The surrogate was pregnant with you
And my heart was full of love!

As the months passed by
Bigger and bigger the surrogate's tummy grew,

I cheerfully prepared for your arrival

I was so excited to meet you!

The day you were born

My dream of having a child came true,

Daddy was beyond grateful
To finally be able to love, hug and kiss you.

Happy together, we are a family
Daddy's love for you is beyond measure,

We laugh, smile and have fun

Making memories we will always treasure!

JULIE MARIE

I am an infertility advocate
and mother through IVF.

It is my hope that Happy Together
will provide a heartwarming,
family building story for parents
to read with their child
sharing just how much they were
wished for and loved.

Printed in Great Britain
by Amazon

44176032R00018